MW00640613

TREE Of LIFE

THE HUMAN ASCENSION
POETRY - INSPIRATION - SHORT STORIES

LEMUEL LAROCHE

LEMUEL'S
INK

Athens, Georgia

Published in United States by
LEMUEL'S INK
P.O. Box 48911
Athens, GA 30604
www.lemuellaroche.com

Copyright © 2010 by Lemuel LaRoche
All rights reserved.

Tree of Life: The Human Ascension © Lemuel LaRoche,

No part of this book may be used, reproduced or transmitted in any form or
by any means, electronic or mechanical, including photocopy, recording, or
any information storage or retrieval system, without the written permission,
excepting the case of brief quotation in critical article or reviews.

Cover Illustration & Design: Lemuel LaRoche , Gregory Jones
Author Photo: Solestential Studio, LLC
Book Editor: Dr. Anjail Ahmad

ISBN 978-0-9884672-1-7 (paperback)
ISBN 978-0-9884672-0-0 (ebook)

For more information on handcrafted version of Tree of Life:
Human Ascension, visit www.lemuellaroche.com

IN MEMORY OF:

Grandma LaRoche; Grandpa Solomon; Ayyub

We live,
We love,
We laugh,
Then we leave.

This book is dedicated to little Ilyesse and the many generations to come.

For Aunt Safiya,
I wish there were more good spirits like yours in this world.

For Sean Bennett,
"*We were not made for this box,*" I heard that loud and clear.

Never surrender your greatness to the defaults of others.

Prologue

Tree of Life

Branch of Life

Sun Cycle
Great Awakening
Walls of Jericho
Spiritual Freedom
Pride
For the Youth
Lioness
It Was Written
Natural Mystic
Twisted Fate
Spiritual Anchor
Experiment
Precious Seeds
Whips and Chains
Georgia
Vision
Forgotten Wisdom
Grandfather's Wisdom
Your eyes

Branch of Inspiration

About the Author

TREE OF LIFE

A healing force of energy rushed forward into the universe. Nothing knew of its origin, but all aligned with The Balance journeyed forward.

The bees abandoned their honeycombs and swarmed in clouds of hundreds of millions. The queen released her pheromones with a dancing command. Slow and hypnotic was her trance. The rhythm captivated the colony and sent them on an instinctive voyage sealed in their hearts. From above, the ground appeared to be moving while those subject to gravity witnessed the massive march of ants. They marched forward in single file from various colonies across the land as they headed toward the destination sealed in their hearts.

Domesticated dogs barked for freedom throughout the night while household cats scratched feverishly at windowpanes demanding their release to heed the call sealed in their hearts. The birds of the North flew in wide circles in the northeastern skies while the birds of the South flooded the southwestern skies migrating to the destination sealed in their hearts.

The mountains whispered rumors of the millions of silent prints left by their inhibitors, while the trees joyfully gossiped about the harmonious journey taken by predator and prey alike towards the destination sealed in their hearts. The enormous fish of the oceans sent their spirits with the passing birds while the smaller fish of the seas and rivers sent their spirits on the backs of leaping frogs and crawling lizards towards the destinations sealed in their hearts.

The children were accounted for. Many of them followed their favorite animals and birds toward this destination, while the elderly spread the wings of their souls and allowed the wind to carry them to the destination sealed in their hearts. The curiosity propelled some young adults to follow this natural migration while some proceeded with their regularly scheduled program of clocking into work. A few that were still aligned with the universal balance responded to the silent ringing in their ears and thrust their bodies towards the destination set within their spiritual compasses.

The journey brought all from the four corners of the Earth and drew them deep into a secluded forest where they stood before a massive old tree. The birds took their positions on its millions of branches while the various species of animals, insects, and humans sat in perfect harmony surrounding the TREE OF LIFE. All closed their eyes in collective meditation and opened the windows to their hearts.

This is what they heard...

Branch of Life

When the sands of time bury us all, what will be said of YOU

when you are discovered?

Sun Cycle

Oh Divine,

Please shed us one tear drop of spiritual bliss
to purify these lakes of fire.
Serve us one tea spoon of righteous sanity
to calm these seas of confusion.
Pour us one cup of raw truth
to satisfy the multitude in famine.

I swam centuries in frozen water
to rejoice in the era of a new SUN~
Your warm smile melts my frostbitten heart.
Your magnetic rays kiss me
vibrating my melanin,
seducing and spinning open my chakras,
reactivating my true self
and impregnating the vision of GREAT PROPHETS.

I am a slave to your divine love,
A servant to your divine order,
A vessel to the mission of truth.

As I write,
I gladly shed a tear drop of pure harmony
for a World that rotates with hate.
I Proudly serve a tablespoon of untainted bliss
into its ending era of material depression.
I humbly recite one paragraph of truth,
to dismantle an entire system of lies.

Great Awakening

Upon awakening,
the world is colored with a strange hue.
Your eardrums numbed by the poisonous frequencies
spread on the airwaves.
Your visions clogged
by the perversion on television;
Your spirit saddened by the conditions around you.
A new craving begins to stir within your spirit,
yet what you crave is unknown.
You've developed a hunger for something deeper,
still, unknown.

Conversations seem bland, pointless, and empty.
Friendship circles slowly shrinking.
Being alone has become your new peace,
silence, your new song.
Guidance from religious guides suddenly lacks substance,
no longer moving your spirit,
no longer satisfying the question burning inside.
A louder, much clearer voice
begins to echo inward.

The clubs you've enjoyed now drain you.
Surrounded by clones,
carbon copies of latest fashions.
You are speaking less in public.
Inner-standing has become your greatest mystery.

An awakening is taking place within you.
Do not fear your experience;
Do not diagnose yourself with the labels of men;

Do not run from yourself.
Listen and reconnect with that great voice within.
It will not steer you wrong.
Welcome the rising from your death.

Walls of Jericho

Is this the calm before the storm?
Is this the feast before the drought?

Computer chips placed in children
while confusion dances amid your thoughts.
You're ruled towards your regression.
Who dares to stride down the lonely, but righteous road
and away from the system designed
to drain spiritual strength?

Stop exalting that which brings forth material happiness.
The Job within no longer accepts the righteous sacrifice,
nor craves the humble reward.

Jericho's walls,
layered with numerical codes, by Master Masons,
stacked with bricks of deception are falling!

Search your master number
to decode the walls that stunt your spiritual growth.
Decline those delusions,
recapture your righteous mind;
leave the system to its wicked ways.
If there is a word
To squeeze your mighty Spirit back to life,
May my tongue chant it every hour of the day
until the walls of Jericho fall.

May my pen scribe for your awakening;
I offer these pages as my sacrifice.

Spiritual Freedom

Spiritual Lions chase tails of Harlots,
Innocence swallowed
History swallowed by the tales of the HARLOT.

Chained to a foreign tomorrow,
One without hills of discipline
Nor mountains of righteousness.

In AMORAL lands,
We BEG the unholy for Justice and freedom
When it is chiseled in our hearts.

Most High Father,
Rain your tears of truth through these words.
Let it drown our conditioned consciousness;
Let it baptize the poisons of temptation
from our blood streams.

Most High Mother,
Help us heal our spiritual wounds~

The human race is sprinting towards death~
Destruction waits at delusive check points.

HARMONY is a distant voice echoing
From the internal KINGDOM.
Let those with ears hear it;
Let those with eyes see it;
LET THOSE WITH VOICES ECHO IT.

Pride

Lion's of Life;
Lion's of Judah;
Lions lost in numerical Jungles...

Lion's wake up and reclaim your PRIDE.

For the Youth

It is time we stand firm, take a pledge for the youth.
Reverse the conditioning being wedged in the youth.
Destruction is running full fledge at the youth.
Molded insanity now hangs on the edge of the youth.
I tell them freedom is waiting, on the ledge for the youth.
Corporations bring Satan on the sledge for the youth.
Reindeer whose noses are painted red for the youth,
And little leprechauns with green fezzes for the youth.
Tooth fairies, hiding under beds for the youth.
Easter bunnies, laying chocolate eggs for the youth.
While the pastor is yelling, *he died and bled for the youth*,
pharmacies are selling prescription meds to the youth.
Rappers sign record deals to spit death to the youth.
Verbal genocide: they spit lead to the youth.
Load poison in pistols and aim it at the heads of the youth.
While parents unaware of what is being said to the youth.
Still consuming the venom, being spread to the youth.
Unconcerned with the lies that's being read to the youth.
Synthetic burgers and fries are being fed to the youth.
Mothers work double shifts, to bring bread to the youth.
To filling the shoes of the alpha males,
who fled from the youth.
Now in crept the spiders, built webs for the youth:
Built prisons and jails to be the shed for the youth.
Judges drop gavels, tears shed from the youth.
25 to life, years shed from the youth.
While the rest of the world run laps ahead of the youth.

When I try to talk sense, they're dreading the truth.
Become a stream-stress for the Most High,
And thread in the truth.
When the valley of death becomes the highway,

just trail in the truth.
Even if you find yourself alone,
at least you dwelled in the truth.
Don't be a rebel without a cause, rebel in the truth.
Stare wicked in its eyes, and tell them the truth.
This system was built on lies, they want to sell you the truth.
Nomenclature words, to spell you the truth.
Your mind is POWER,
use your voice to nail in the truth.
Be engaged to righteousness-be wed in the truth.
Be protected by the greater light-be held in the truth.

LIONESS

Walk with elegance towards your mighty lion.
May the lamb and sheep find a pure Sheppard to follow,
but be cautious of who you choose to guide your soul.
For many are blindfolded to truth
and slaves to the ram's horn.

Know thyself when paddling in the ocean with sharks,
find your strength and swim forth.
Know thyself when you walk amongst the Lions of Judah,
stamp your print in destiny.

Progression is my roaring call,
regression in thy spirit will lead to thy fall.
Your mind has become your prison,
your concepts are the cement walls.
Your perceptions are your bars.
Free yourself from yourself.
Find your strength.
Redefine your vision.

I cannot carry you.
For you too were given legs to stand,
And you too are strong enough to walk,
I cannot hold your hands in this season of your regression,
the stem of your flower is consumed by too many thorns.
I have seen the path carved for my journey.

I know my purpose.
I am learning my strength.
My seeds are not meant to flourish in the soil of Babylon,
but surely
this lion will replenish the earth.

It was WRITTEN

You sailed satellites into the body of my universe
to monitor movements,
but you cannot yield what is to be.
Erected conditioning institutions to mis-educate
and suppress the divine within,
but you cannot yield what is to come.

Propagated fear, self-hatred,
racial tension to spark racial wars,
but you will not yield the divine harmony that is destined.
You can drain the planet for all of its natural resources,
only to drown in your pool of power,
choke by your own gluttony.

It is clear that you are an agent of death;
plague time with wars and bloodshed,
create NEWS stations to repetitiously,
advertise and monitor this death.
You can pillage nations under the banner of FREEDOM,
but you cannot stop nor trick karma.

What will be must be--
It is written in every book,
on every ancient wall,
under every buried rock,
between the crevice of every new spirit born,
in every spoken and unspoken language:
The era of peace will shine again.
Inheritance of the earth awaits the meek.
This you cannot and will not stop.

Fear not children of the light.
For this beast is self-destructing.
Stand not in the shadow of his fallen building.
We must rebuild;
We must rename;
We must play our position in righteousness.

Natural Mystic

Beneath the flesh, the blood slowly boiling,
heart roaring with passionate steam,
melting the cold web of Babylon
releasing another captive child's dream.
We've walked on sands left no footprints,
tasted salvation in clouds.
We pray for rain of change
as our silence echo aloud.
May it bring down the wicked walls of Jericho,
turn inward the stomach of every brick;
impregnate new consciousness in humanity,
lured in perverted playgrounds of tricks.

Twisted Fate

The cheering spider chants her joy,
thankful to the wind for the supper that landed on her web.

The fearful fly is chanting his last prayer,
begging one more hour from life,
cursing the wind for its misguidance,
yet slowly accepting his fate: the spider's meal.

We shed tears in joy,
shed tears in pain;
find sanity in the web of love,
where some become more insane.

Thankful like the spider for life's small blessings,
yet doomed as the fly, trapped in karma's web.

Spiritual Anchor

Still you sail through life without a spiritual anchor,
growing towards death like trees without roots;
naked as pages produced by ink-less pens
as civilizations vanish from history's canvas.

Who will scribe your story in the winds of time?

Beware of he who appears as a social lamb
and spreads folklore like the howling wolf;
free your soul from broken ballads.

Even after the season of shedding,
the snake is still the snake.
When surrounded by the dead,
be as the condor and remove the carcass from the roads
on which your children play.

Flush the fables from your conscious mind,
place a filter at the doorway of your subconscious;
For as the Gold fish's growth is stunted
to the size of the fish tank,
So is the mind craftily boxed into its think tank.

The universe is your spiritual abode.
Let not the ocean, nor the sky become your web.
Sacrifice your flesh for the channeling of divine truth.

Experiment

From Prince to Pimps
He bought new shoes for his car
While his child stood bare footed
He stared me dead in my eyes
And called himself a real man

From Queen hood to hood rat
Her self-esteem is measured
By the size of the cushion she uses
to support her back while defecating
She looked me in my eyes
And demanded my respect

From pyramids to projects
He shot another brother for his projects
A building on a plot of land he does not own
He stared the judge in the eyes
and told his lawyer
he will gladly do the jail time for his projects
A place he didn't name
Her mind is the product of the same project
Their character was socially engineered in a project
Someone's project;
someone's experiment.

Precious Seeds

Words molded into form
to inform the seed.

Be wary of the plots sown to capture your soul
by secret societies like "Skull and Bones."
Rappers of death
use words to wrap the texture of seeds
with shirts, belts and hats with skulls and bones on it.

Drained in this spiritual warfare,
I pose this question!
Do you, too, blind yourself with this tragic reality,
using your energy to chase paper shredded from trees
that bring forth abundance of material possessions?
Or do you sow a net with your words
and use it to catch something much more valuable-
the minds and souls of our youth.

Whips and Chains

While scrolling through the painful pages of history,
I'm reminded of the struggles of my forefathers.
They ran from,
they died from
Whips and Chains.
Spiritually confused and mentally misguided,
I watch my generation
And the footprints we leave behind,
running towards,
dying for,
Whips (Cars) and Chains (Jewelry).

Georgia

Spread my ashes over the mountains of North Georgia,
bury me deep in confederate clay.
Let my bones purify the red soil,
cursed by the trees that unwillingly partook
in legal lynching
and those poor trees carved and ash away
in fire worship rituals.
Burning crosses display a deep devotion and love for GOD,
yet reveals a deeper hate for GOD's creation
of the darker brothers.
Daddy's doctrine still rots the core
of the sweet and tender peach,
Born with love in hearts,
with warm spirits baked by the Southern Sun
and cooled by the mist of the Savannah breeze.
I lost my patience on the concrete block in a cold city
and found her while holding a fishing rod
on the Oconee Creek.
It was there that the trees made this confession,
then the flapping of an old flag broke my mediation,
Worn on the skull of innocent and impressionable cub
Who stared at me with young eyes fixed with old hate.
It is our generation who must break our father's curse;
who must climb out of the Hate Holes they dug in our hearts
so we can, once again, LOVE WHOLE.

Vision

The old are dreaming dreams,
the young are buried with untouched visions.
Branches: they fall from the family tree.
Generations of fathers: are buried in prisons.
Was this the dream of Dr. King?
Was this the vision of Patrice Lumumba?

I gaze at the dim twilight, foreign to my eyes.
Watch life hang like fringes on Hebrews.

Unchaining the unborn.

From articulated lies,
the sight of war fogs the horizon
instigated by the reptile's tongue of death.
They slither venom in subconscious mind
Activating the reptile brain in the child of destiny.

I stand armored in truth with fringes on my waist,
growing impatient for my inheritance.
Let he with vision plant the seed of forgotten courage;
let she with righteous aim deliver forth
the sons and daughters of destiny.

Forgotten Wisdom

Before the youth can grasp the concept of reading,
the elders must first grasp the concept of writing
from the well of forgotten wisdom.
For this is the essence of The MOST HIGH
passing through generations.

Grandfather's Wisdom

A grandparent conversing with a grandchild is the sound of the Divine speaking through time.

A college student heavily inspired by the words of his pastor met with his grandfather one weekend while away from school. He awakened his Grandfather early one Sunday morning and asked him to go to church with him. *Today is the Lord's Day,* he recited. *Today we must go to church and praise him. I want you to meet my pastor; he is a great man of God.*

The grandfather simply replied: *sit down for a second my boy.* He spoke with deep wisdom to his grandson.

He said...
We share different concepts of the Divine my boy. I can clearly hear the words of the DIVINE in the sound of a leaf landing on the ground after a long dance with the wind. I feel the rich essence of the DIVINE in the texture of the same wind on a breezeless day. But to you my boy, God is a name, God is an image, God is a religion and God is a book. Your God is the giver of material wealth, although the road of materialism is filled with spiritual suicide. In our small hour of existence, a man is now defined and respected for his possessions. Education is what marks the intellect of the modern man. You need elaborate pieces of paper with approval signatures from men to be of worth. My son, you live in a fabricated reality. You live in a time where mothers are given monthly wages to medicate their children, and the fruits we buy no longer have seeds in it. Explain this my boy, how

could another man possibly give me understanding of God in this sort of reality? I want you to tell me how God speaks to you, not how God speaks through another.

Your Eyes

He said...
He has seen many sunny days turn to storms.
He then shut the old windows to his soul
and smiled as he took his final breath.
Two seconds forward,
the cry of a new born baby boy echoed from a distant universe
and brought an abundance of sun shine
into my hour of depression.
I paused to ponder on the shedding cycle called life
where the elder departed with a smile
and the new born was thrust into this realm
with eyes full of tears.
A society where seeds are absent from grapes,
Goldfish tarnishing in rotten lakes,
unconditional love drained from the heart's chamber
and righteousness lays dormant in shells of the mortal.
When did humanity forget that Life is a leaf?
Life is also the branch that carries the leaf,
the tree that holds her branches,
and the forest that mothers her trees.
Do not allow the morning fogs to blur your spiritual vision,
for you are the vine that will produce the seed-full grape,
the truth that will mature the goldfish,
the flood of love to refill the vacant heart,
and the trumpet to awaken the sleeping giants.
Stare not at life through the painful eyes of the passing elder,
nor the joyful tears of the coming youth,
but from the eyes you were given.

Branch of Truth

The only thing one hundred percent in this world is truth. Once diluted, it changes form.

The Ant and the Mountain

How does an ant move a mountain? A grain at a time.

Massive and marvelous is the mountain that stood before this ant. He gazed at its height until his eyes meet with the source of life. UNAFRAID and UNCONQUERED is his spirit, as he marches toward his mission as if controlled by an unseen force. It may take this ant a billion years to accomplish this mission while he marches each day with purpose. A sense of pride marks each step as he follows the instructions of his inner voice, which communicates a mission (A message) to us all. Some of us hear it while others detach from it.

Meanwhile...

Dreadful and draining are the days that await her. She gazes at the mountain of paper work placed on her desk to welcome her bright morning. UNINSPIRED and UNMOTIVATED, she dragged herself through the office as if controlled by a well-known monster called DEBT. It will take her forty years to climb out of her accumulated debt while she clocks in and out daily with feelings of deep disgust. Cold feelings of enslavement haunt her as she follows the instructions of her government conditioning (education), which has conditioned us all. Some of us cling to it, while others detach from it.

Imitation Life

When the taxes taken from our weekly checks
are used to build prisons that incarcerate us,
develop school curriculums to educate us,
pay for the salaries and training
of racist police officers that target us,
then I must conclude
that we are financing our own destruction.

A degree earned from the prestigious colleges and universities
are merely pieces of paper
which require the signature of men...
ONLY MEN~
These mortal masters
will never expose us to our GODLY identity,
for they possess finite knowledge,
finite wisdom and finite inner-standing,
which they've carefully wrapped
under layers of social conditioning,
colorfully camouflaged as School Spirit,
Athletic Altars, Gladiator Worship, Packed Coliseums,
Greek Life and Letters to symbolize brotherhood
through broken pride,
virgin innocence ripped
when carnal seeds and beer kegs collide.
Drunken frat boys become scholars of our Moral Authority
and are given the power to enforce policies
that dictate how we should raise our children.

Mental Holocaust committed in Class Chambers
where the souls of students are solicited to CORPORATIONS
that suck dry their humanity through their "STRAW MAN."

Cap and gown like black hooded robes
worn in public initiations,
where new graduates are given Degrees
as janitorial Keys to the TOWER OF BABEL.
Every floor layered with secret handshakes and coded
language to control the perception and behavior
of the sleeping masses.

We see clearly the signs of deteriorating times,
but still we recycle our children
through the revolving doors of spiritual death.
We proudly encourage them to close their universal portals of
Infinite Knowledge, Infinite Wisdom
And Infinite Inner-Standing
that guides them through their Intuition,
but they can trade it all for a college Tuition
so that they, too, can purchase expensive cars,
elaborate homes,
25 years of student loans
that fuels the engine of this capitalist system
operating under the premise that
MONEY DOES GROW ON YOUR FAMILY TREE.
Every branch of your sanity shredded into currency
that rotates from pay check to taxes,
taxes to government, government to institutions,
institutions to employers, employers to employees.
And when your candle of LIFE melts away
or is blown out by the same breath that blew life into you,
we leave behind trails of material possessions,
wills that divide families,
bills that drive us to financial insanity.
Then we're given Prescription Pills to "balance" our humanity,
all because we've chosen to suffocate
our reality with the pillows of this IMITATION LIFE.

Life is not your expensive vehicle
that eventually will rust in the windows of a decade.

Life is not your mansion
which has become your prison by enslaving you
with the chains of its mortgage.
Life is not your two to twelve year degree
sewn into your identity.
Life is that spark that peels back your eye lids
to the morning sun.
Life is the two second vision of clarity,
piercing through your cloudiest moments.
Life is the voice of inspiration,
constantly drawing you back to your center.
Life is and Life will become
when you learn to listen and function
at your highest spiritual potential.

Uncivilized Jungle

In the mechanical jungle, animals come out to play.
Eagle soars the sky with broken wings
and bloodthirsty talons.
Beneath her wings,
fleas grow to be elephants and donkeys;
perverted elephants play footsie in bathroom stalls
long trunks to drain the morale of a nation.
The Jackass is in search of identity,
while claiming to carry the fearful nation.
The mountain leopards call the desert lions "Terrorists,"
cattle consumed by vultures,
venomous snakes poisoning cultures,
Black panthers were slain,
packs of wolves drowned in their trail of tears.
Dogs roaming streets without direction,
Beautiful cardinal staring through a carnal mirror,
pecking at her own reflection.
Pigs enforcing the policies of corporate sharks,
the wise owls afraid to speak,
while the trees cry fogs of fire for change...

Are you ready to burn down the forest and replenish it?

Numerical Prison

I received a letter from the Department of Motor vehicles.
It stated that camera 0302020100
on Interstate 85 N
clocked me speeding 85 mph in an 55 mph zone.
It recorded my license plate number,
ran it through the central computer database,
which matched it with my driver's license
and then mailed me a citation
asking for me to appear in court
or pay the fine of $145.55.
I replied with a letter of my own.
I wrote: Big Brother, Big brother,
I am man, not statistic.
Big Brother, Big Brother,
I was molded from flesh,
not numerical digits.
I swam from my mother's womb into a sea of numbers.
When you see me,
your eyes register a tall slim,
caramel, brown skin brother
born and raised in Brooklyn, New York,
now residing in Athens, Georgia.
And I was just another chocolate chip
on the University of Georgia's cookie.
When Big Brother sees,
he doesn't recognize my locs,
the scars on my flesh.
He doesn't feel the fire raging in my chest.
He only recognizes codes;
he reads only numbers
to identify me as 009 90 9999,

born 09 09 1999,
in state code 13,
area code 718,
zip code 11221,
now residing in state code 36
area code 706,
zip code 30606.
My race makes up 30% of state code 36's population,
1.9% of school code 000198,
and 71.3% of prison code 00203 03 002100.
I swam from my mother's womb into a sea of #.
I swam from nature's womb into a numerical prison.
The satellite is my probation officer,
and monitors me through the GPS system
and traces my voice pattern
every time I use 0777 123 9889.
Humanity Wake up,
untangle yourself from this digital web.
Free yourself from this ocean of #'s
where over 70% of the western world
is drowning in debt;
Free yourself from this numerical prison,
where at birth you are provided with a birth certificate
and tracked through a set of numbers
as a form of identification
similar to the intake process of incarceration.
Big brother, send me a P.O. address
so I can mail you back your social security card,
these bank cards to track my spending habits,
gas cards to monitor my traveling habits,
supermarket cards to track my dietary habits,
so that you can begin to speak to me as a person.

The spider in the storm

Category four was the label given to the coming storm.
"Only one notch below THE FINGERS OF GOD,"
yelled the weather man in a terrifying tone.

His warning was sent forward through various frequencies
and triggered a man to take a hammer
and bang a nail into the right shoulder of a wooden plank,
to protect the glass window to his business from the coming
storm.

That same frequency
made another man pack the belongings of his family
onto the hood of his small vehicle and join the pack of cars
heading away from the coming storm.

While the people panicked from the warning,
the tiny spider added another layer to the coat of her web
and began wrapping her blessings in the form of
small insects blown into her web by the strong wind.

The storm touched the shores with deep anger.
Some say the bones of the slaves dumped into the ocean
centuries prior, wielded their fury.
They yelled aloud for all to hear;
those who chose to ride out the storm heard the frustration.
The message was loud and clear:
"CHANGE YOUR WAYS OR PERISH."

The power peeled the roof off brick homes,
while the spider web danced in perfect harmony
with the melody of the storm.

The force collapsed the foundation of cement buildings
and threw a mid-size truck through a boarded storefront,
While the spider sat in perfect prostration
meditating through the storm.

When the tears of the storm calm and passed,
the death toll was estimated in the hundreds,
thousands were reported as injured.
Property damages soared in the millions
as the spider slowly unwrapped her meal to begin
her peaceful feast.

Thorns

If my frame of thinking is a thorn on the road heading towards delusional bliss, then I pray daily for the children to walk with bare feet.

Checkmate

The chessboard is full of lost pawns
Strong queens become dancing slaves to the dollar
Fallen Kings stumble the block with beer bottles
Drowned in their forgotten Greatness
Broken Castles are crack houses
Broken communities crack spirits
Perverted bishops fish for innocent souls with religious rods
Chanting the sweet words of God with snake like tongues
Blind Knights remembered in eulogies
Our children stray away in the blind nights
Their carcasses left for corporate vultures
Hovering over the eagles nest
Trapped in small cubes on the chess board without a strategy
Checkmate
Cell mates

Free yourself from those squares
Climb swiftly out of Babylon's boxes.

Crossroads

Once the veil lifted from my spiritual eye,
the crossroad of life became more vivid.
On the road heading left,
flashed everything I've been conditioned to love:
temptation-molesting little cubs.
On the road heading right,
I saw a new world waiting to be built:
populated with tomorrow's pride.
I tasted a freedom unseasoned by Hell's Kitchen,
a freedom undefined by Webster's dictionary.

Do I place the veil over my eyes
and travel left to further my spiritual regression
or do I proceed to process self discipline?
Meditate in silence while journeying inward.
A journey to travel without feet,
without flesh.
A journey to meet my highest self for clarity--
this is my exodus,
Mother Africa called me in my dream.
The ringing in my left ears grows louder.
Is this the final trumpet blown by the angels?

I wonder,
as I stand witness to the fall of the great Babylon.
In her economic meltdown,
still they party like dimming rock stars.
Some see the coming drought.
Others wallow in the rain of confusion.
Babylon is burning! I yell.
GET OUT OF HER.

Exodus

I glance out of the window of a small room
in a burning building,
while residents in the same house
rest comfortably through the night.
Can they not see the ashes of the stained yesterday?
Can they not feel the flame of temptation
that burns their righteous minds?
Can they not smell the stench of the hell
they have grown to love?

Precious Flowers

You criticize the hell surrounding you,
but yearn to swim through the flames of fame
till your temple is a charity to the wicked.

Precious flowers, chopped by life's cleaver,
bated by the long tongues of chameleons,
dethroning their inner sense
Addicting them to the ignorance eroding their innocence.
Precious flowers, self-love is essential for growth.
Water your hearts with respect
and watch how high the mountain of beauty
will grow within you.
Precious flowers, know the essence that stirs your strength,
which carries you through these booby-trapped ghettos,
crack infested communities,
while still you blossom with smiles.
Precious flowers,
how can I not be thankful to the fingers of creation
for fashioning you.
You birthed humanity through pain,
yet still shelter love in your sacred chapel.

Precious flowers, even after the cold season of pillage
and countless hours of rape by your offspring,
you shower vibrant colors and fragrances of love.

Precious flowers, let go of the winter's curse
and let not your stamens be polluted by the poisonous pollen.

Dry Tears

I shed a dry tear for the coming generation,
future kings refashioned into one-armed zombies.
He walks with an angry face, rapping to himself,
"I'm a thug nigga."
"I'm a blood killah."
He's lying to himself.
"I trap that white,"
"I clap guns all night."
Young boy, stop lying to yourself.
You were born and equipped with two hands,
but you've allowed fashion to employ one hand;
one hand to scratch or twist your hair
and the other used to hold your pants up.
The names and faces change,
but the behaviors are the same from city to city.
You never learned how to use a belt,
and still you're trying to convince me that you're real...
"Real" lost, I see.
Latest fashion got you looking
"Real" stupid these days.
He stares in the mirror daily
seeing his favorite rapper as his reflection.
His highest aspiration is to be caged like an animal.
This he believes is what makes him real;
this he believes will attract his queen;
this is all he knows;
this is all he sees in his inner mirror
and it is he who will carry my torch into tomorrow's darkness.
It is he who will one day father a child;
it is he we must reach for; it is he who must grow.
I shed dry tears for the coming generation.

Second Death

The scriptures write about two deaths: the death of the physical body before transcending to the spiritual realm, and the death of the soul when the person aligns with dark forces. I want to introduce you to a death I witness every day.

Every ladder I climb, leads me to the same floor:
socially constructed ghettos,
the inhabitants adapt to mentalities that are very poor.
Roaming streets without vision,
Foundation is unknown.
Existing to replenish pockets of corporations
Psychologically programmed to reject own.
From birth, conditioned
to conform to pre-established ideologies
that rode backs of blacks like camels,
Now fully dependent
on a system that defines us as animals.
Blocks parallel to zoos,
Barbed wires, cameras placed on gates.
Armed zookeepers with badges,
trained to shoot when they sense retaliate.
Handcuffed me,
handcuff black children and label us inmates.
In this zoo-keeper's mind,
community struggle is a mirage,
but we view the picture as something realistic,
In it, we search for painted leap portals
to quantum leap into conditions not so animalistic.
Reality placed us back in black traps, government statistics
A high percentage of dark doubles, struggles in closed tunnels,
living in cages, placed in holes like rats.
Shortage of cheese force families

into government facilities:
government housing PROJECTS
where we are sold guns, given crack
For a piece of that sweet ole America pie
plot at our neighbors' goods and attack.
So now,
I watch with bare eyes and on television screens,
brothers dying for a slice,
dying from lack of positive paternal advice.
born in mental comas, when they die,
they die twice.
A second death.

Green Haven Correctional Facility

I dozed off after a long visit
and woke up on a slave ship,
sailing back to the auction block.
Besides the navigator,
I am the only warrior left on a ship
of women and children.
My mind wondered, within its wander:
do I belong on the other side of the gate
with the captured warriors?
Or on this sail back to the slave fields
with the women and children?
Where red, white and blue sirens howl to scare the young
and crack reality incubates the psyche.
The answer sprang from my soul like flowers in spring fields
and de-thawed my frozen mind with rays of clarity.
I heard the voice clearly as it whispered,
Someone has to protect them.

Don't shoot with that Gun

Are you aware that infants and toddlers are searched
with metal detectors
upon visiting their fathers, mothers,
sisters, brothers, uncles and aunts behind bars.
When they return into this fixed labyrinth called society,
they are told to shoot for the stars.
How are they to shoot for the stars
if not given the proper ammunition?
How can we properly substitute their desperate thoughts,
if we're residing in these deficient positions?
Can someone please show me how to build a better tomorrow
with yesterday's bricks.
And introduce me to something better to teach my children
than they were the slaves of whips.
I could teach them how to survive,
but who chooses the jails and prison cells they will survive in?
and how can this society accept their innocence
when it confuse negativity with the color of their dark skin?
I could teach them about life
and how their social class will predict their obstacles.
I can't choose their beliefs,
But hope the decisions they make are logical.
I finally understand the pain that causes parents
to cry ponds into lakes.
How do you change the direction of your children
when they have learned to love and imitate your mistakes?
Can you truly blame them
for their lack of motivation and absence of fear?
How much would you choose to accomplish
after constantly hearing that the end days are near?
When your children begin to shoot for a better tomorrow,

please remove the guns from the shelf.
Replace it with wisdom and pride,
and teach them about way to master self.
We build a better future
when we first find and build ourselves.

Inner Self

I calmly ask that you rip the pages of barbaric conditioning
and rediscover your righteous self.
Scrape the dry blood of this dying nation off your soul.
Consume with grace from the spiritual tree of life,
raise your vibrations,
and begin the metamorphosis into your anointed self.
Place crystals on your chakras
and you will stop confusing visions with dreams,
reverse the backward spinning of your thoughts
and impregnate righteous vision into the new twilight.
Channel in those benevolent beings who await your
awakening.
Challenge and control your delirium winds.
Peel off the layers of confusion foiled upon your inner mind.
We are living in the era, which requires the real, you.
Daily, men are buried in the earth,
while the body becomes the compost to fertilize the soil,
preparing for the harvest of the potent seeds.

Eternal

A swift blink and I stand an old man behind a podium.
How fast does life's curtain fall,
the moon now a grain of salt
in the bland universe
where I feast with my guardians in the cosmos,
thanking them for their protection.
Still a memory beseeched me,
of trees that grow from dirt
which I was once formed.
Gender-less but fruitful as they sway,
obeying the commandment of universal balance:
I am a part of you, as you are a part of me.
Then the earth recalls its borrowed flesh.
The ground welcomes my coffin,
a wooden table for parasites to feast,
releasing my once trapped spirit.
I am still a part of you, as you are a part of me.
Now to eternity I travel forward,
leaving positive prints through realms and dimensions.
Traces of my presence chipped in memories,
float like kites across the burning blue sky.
Show me where the ashes of time are piled
and I'll show you green mountains
where our shells shrink to wrinkled coats
and are worn by our wisdom.

Seeds in the Earth

I am a seed that burst from a rotten fruit;
a fruit that fell from a bad tree;
a tree planted in damaged soil;
but with my seed,
I will grow a better tree.

SEEDS

I have seen a small seed grow into a giant tree with the proper nutrients. It now shades the people, animals and grass from the burning sun. It now produces oxygen, and provides shelter for generations of squirrels, birds and insects. It helps to beautify the canvas around me.

I have also seen a small seed with the wrong guidance grow inside of a prison cell. He now stands in the shade of a cement wall. He shares oxygen with numerous seeds. He is the last of his family tree because, at the age of 17, he was sentenced to life without parole. The dull canvas around him grows darker as he drowns in tears of regret.

We must raise our seeds to become strong trees.

Guidance

If you carry your child for too long,
they may never learn to use their legs.
Teach your children to walk properly,
for they may carry you during your vulnerable age.

Fingers

Slender his frame,
fist balled with pain.
He stands
as the mantis ready to strike its prey.

Open your fist young warrior,
let the winds tickle your palm.
Point your finger not at your enemy.
but inward for clarity.

Like the tongue used to chant truth,
the fingers too have their special purpose.
It is the fingers that seduce the clarinet
and stimulate the guitar's soul,
to translate the heart's rhythmic plight.
The fingers also command the bow, massaging the violin
as they do the pen that scribes

Unleash your anger not with your fist,
but through your pen,
by way of your fingers.

Season of Silence

The spring smiles a new sun's light
A righteous aura to heal the frostbitten past
The spirit of divine truth evaporates into the mist
And rides back to earth on the coming rain
Let it refill the cups drained of life
Let it nourish the seeds hibernating in the sleeping shell

Sober from your intoxication
Close your eyes to the winter's moon
Inhale the pollen of righteous rejuvenation
For a new world trails the passing storm
The reigns of yesterday will whisper no more

A new leaf sprouts in the rain forest
It grows patiently toward the spring's sun
The trees sway with joy to the silent wind
And I, too, dance in silence to the same tune

It is in this silence that life reveals its deepest secrets
And engages the caterpillar's metamorphosis
The silence that uproots the lotus flower from mud
And warns you that something is terribly wrong

In this silence you will be given the answers
In its depth
You, too, will change
Listen deeply with your heart
And you will hear it.

Change

Judge not by one's appearance.
Eat not from the plates of death.

The eyes of your inner giant peel open slowly
and you will be given enormous visions.
The great spirit is awakening within you.
Raise your vibration to welcome your new guides.
Move steady towards your growth.
Speak with your mighty tongue.
They not in tune with the universal order
will be FORCED to change.

Positive Affirmation

I can change the world,
and I will begin with one youth at a time.

Balance

The SUN is my vibrant spirit,
The MOON is my pale coal,
The EARTH is my precious flower,
The OCEAN is my blue soul.

YOU

If the caterpillar can break the chain of gravity
to morph into a beautiful butterfly
with two weeks of silence,
just imagine the greater you
waiting upon your metamorphoses.
With two weeks of tranquility, deep meditation,
you will overcome and conquer all hindrances.

The caterpillar traveled inward for nine to fourteen days
and flew out with radiant colors.
The caterpillar's journey is placed as a reminder
that everything we need and search for is within us.

Search not for the given answer.
Instead quest for the right question,
and the answer will be given.
Ask not for an abundance of material wealth,
but for eternal happiness, love and peace.

Conger not the spirit of greed;
filter your skies from the pollution;
fast from television and radio;
ascend from negative vibration.

Journey inward, along the highway of serenity,
and bring forth your placid dreams.
Challenge your uncouth perceptions;
break the curse of your degeneration.
Your instructions await you in your silence.
Go within and hear,
Like the caterpillar,
you too will make your metamorp

Branch of Pain

When the fingers that heal become the claws that scar,
the hand must be chopped off.

A New Day

My eyes have seen both great and dreadful days.
The Eagle's claw wedged deep in my soul,
I grow stronger with each scar.

The children laugh in my dreams;
scream in my reality,
and stare with zombie eyes
intoxicated on the legal prescriptions of men.
If removing one brick can begin the crumbling
of the wicked system,
help me find that brick.

Help me save the sleeping children,
paralyzed and persuaded by the Illusionist.

If one small seed can grow the big and mighty apple tree,
cannot one child illuminate this world of darkness?
Are our children not worth the sacrifice?
A new day is upon us.

Cell Cycles

Dark daydreams fuse on cell walls.
Cement bricks highlight the motion picture
projected in old memories.
The shadow becomes the mirror's reflection
and grows smaller in the direction of death.
Young and old hearts are scarred
in subconscious battlefields;
affliction in the youth's soul,
addiction in the aged sole of the father.

Fathers and sons trapped in mental chains,
exiled from their potential,
herded for financial slaughter
disguised as rehabilitation,
divided as profits,
to be served on capitalist plates.
Corporations flourish while communities drained dry,
pipelines from projects to prisons fill justice's cup.

Warm black feet meet cold roads,
socks pulled off by "Education,"
tears overflowing,
cracking the wells that once held them.
Black child of the golden sun,
cut down the red curtain of illusion.
Do not let the illusionist steal your imagination.

In Flight

Every strand of DNA reminds my wings to fly away,
but I have been blinded to the direction back home.
Until I find that right path,
I am afflicted by each day's turbulent winds,
slowly shedding feathers of my wings,
peeling bare my innocence.

I am now a wing-less bird
who sees the direction home,
a trail too far to foot.
In time I will grow new feathers.
In time I will sprout new wings.
Who cares to join me on the journey back?
Who else is willing to fly away?

Psychological Hangings

Scars wrapped around the heart of this woman
as she watched the father of her children
HANGING lifeless from the arms of a tree
by the three bitter and hateful men that raped her.

She dig deep within her soul,
gathered the strength of her Great Ancestors,
and crawled like a wounded dog
towards the shack she called home.

Once there,
she leaned on her scraped and bloody knees,
raised her desperate arms to the heavens,
cried and prayed to the picture of a white man
HANGING on her kitchen wall.

Mother Afrika

America, my stepfather,
speaks harshly of Mother Afrika.
He claims she walks with a primitive limp.
Since birth, I've been clogged with stories
of her hunger and dry bones,
never mentioned was the richness of her blood
and her fertile breast.
Still my mother's heart is mined
and drained for resources;
demoralized with experimental thoughts.
He told me that he adopted me to "civilize" me,
and she is paying for my child support.
He treats me like he hates my mother
while sorrowing over his kidnapping guilt.
Now that I'm a man, I've grown inquisitive for the truth,
searching through the rubble of my mother's culture
and the buried archives of my immoral father's lies.
My mother's blood still flows richly through me,
but I have adopted my step-father's mind.
My heart still beats to my mother's drums,
but now we speak with different tongues,
deleted dialects and authentic traditions
replaced by folktale,
devotion to my ignorance.
With diligence, I search for my mother's prints,
but through the hate of my step father.
Will I ever uncovered the buried truth
and fully understand her version of the story?

My Cry (South Africa)

I call your attention to the winding trail of freedom road
that dumped families into tiny tin shacks
in townships of SOWETO,
townships of ALEXANDRA,
Townships across Southern Africa,
where beautiful brown, black and colored children
inherit the poverty of their mothers,
who have inherited the struggles of their fathers,
Whose fertile lands and rich spirit were swallowed
by the greed of APARTHEID.
They are reminded daily to forgive,
forget and psychologically accept
their poor conditions, as rites of passage
into the fabricated heavens of their colonizer's religion.
Can someone please show me how to bring an end to this
vicious and immoral cycle
without pointing to the same educational system
that stole your natural birthright,
sewn to your soul a foreign and empty name,
demonized your cultural traditions,
and conditioned you against yourself.
Your lamb's wool like locs,
the many waters of your tone and
beautiful brown complexion,
are evidence of your indigenous claims to the land,
but the mind has become a colonial property
captured inside of interNETS,
wrapped tightly for moral draining in social WEBsites,
and drugged by satellite transmitted images
through tubes of deception
to enhance your intoxication for material wealth.
It saddens my soul to see you assimilate the ways of

"culture vultures"
and summon your spirits to death in the name of
soul-less civilization.
Oh children of DESTINY,
when the bright lights of illusion blind your eyesight
and divert you from the breeding ground of mental
and spiritual liberation,
use your insight to recover and uncover your righteous self.
Love not the culture of death
fed to you by your spiritual nemesis,
but if you so choose to love your enemy,
Please,

LOVE YOURSELF MORE!

Dying Weeds

She verbally vomited
her inclement experience into my dry ears.
Her words roughly scratched the surface of my ear drums,
stirring waves of sorrow within my well of emotion.
Her verbs slowly picking at my chambers of tears.
sending a flood of pain down my desolated cheeks.

In the midst of her cry,
I could hear her warm spirit yelling for freedom,
a skeleton pounding to be released
from broken closet doors.
She rejected my compassionate hug,
stared at me with dead eyes
and uttered,
no ship can withstand the stormy clouds of my past.
The wickedness of MAN
has scarred too many earths
and has dimmed many sons.

It would take Two Thousand seasons
for earth to bare an innocent and righteous fruit.
Her virgin flower was picked by carnal hands
and she was left a dying weed.

Oh Most High,
please protect the flowers that grow
in the Fallen system of Babylon.
Allow their wombs to bring forth fruits
for the replenishment of Genesis.

The Cries of that Woman

I would hear her curse the earth with harsh words
for the creation of my kind.
Patient she has been, hurt she has been,
for a good man she has sought
but could not find.
Her rage is full of fire and her heart is filled with pain.
She keeps a promise in her head;
She said she will never again be harmed
by the charm of men.
Before that, she would rather be dead.
She was raped several times,
divorced twice.
She stood as the symbol of an abused wife
and she said that men were to blame,
for with men there came
most of the destruction she faced in her life.
For the nine months of her pregnancy,
I watched her struggle alone,
awaiting the daughter she expected.
When she saw men, she spat on their feet.
Towards men, she lost all respect.
At boys she fussed,
at men she cussed
to released the hatred that crawled deep beneath her skin.
At night she prayed to rid the planet from men.
She believed we were all mold by sin.
Her dream and plan
formed from her hate for man
as she drowned in her realm of hurt.
For the sake of her desired daughter,
she begged the heavens for a new design.
She said that Adam was worth dirt.

Now that day came to pass,
her prayer was heard.
So were her cries when the labor was done.
What lesson did she prepare for her future,
because she gave birth to a SON.

ARK

She sold the ark of her covenant
for a role she now regrets.
Released from the web of eroticism,
she lives her life in an empty shell.
Naked rooms in her once sacred mansion,
every tear shed
hoping will cleanse her soul.
Welted scars, a reminder of the stain in her life,
her days like the days of Noah.
There's so much rain in her life.

False Prophet

I watched
the blanket of spirituality was folded, and misused.
No longer does it warm the children
it once promised to protect.
It now veils chicanery in the minds of MEN.

I watched
a leaf fall from an old tree,
stood motionless in the wind,
forgotten origin.

Innocent are the children's minds,
warmed with fear redefined as loyalty
while their fragile frames are abused
by aberrant mind-state.

I watched and I cried
seas that I must eventually swim across,
pour acerbic ink to impregnate awareness,
but eyes that once could see, are wide closed.
Charisma cocoons their eardrum,
souls now sandals in the sand.

Where does the altruist go for healing?

Vanishing Dreams

Awakened by life's force
last night, I dreamt of playgrounds empty of frolic,
neighboring a grave yard scented with garlic.
Lying in between,
I saw stream after stream of dying dreams.
Floating back to its source
upon morning's visit,
each dream became a mourning reality,
thus I dream no more.

Fallen Mansion

I am the cracked brick holding together a fallen palace.
Useless and unappreciated.
Animosity brewing in the stomach of every brick.
They whisper to me,
"when I crumble, the palace will be forgotten by time."

I stand cemented with millions,
tired of the mistreatment,
drained from the deceit,
frustrated with decorated lies.
The mansion owner walks lightheartedly,
cloaks me with colorful imaginations,
convinced that new summer coats will keep me intact.
The stress crack has reached my back.
Am I prepared for the fall and the rebuilding?
Are we prepared for the prophesied demolition
and the building of a greater mansion?
Will you survive the great fall?

Legal Slavery

Not in my back yard, he said.
Yet the chain of Supply and Demand
wraps tightly around the soul of my village.
Prisons are products advertised to children,
the community targeted by corporate vultures,
banking accounts leeched onto the poverty stricken
profits gained off misconduct.

Where is the social and soulful drum?
Beating silent in the slum
and replaced with synthetic tunes to trap the beta waves.
Plastic lifestyle suffocates the innate breath,
juxtaposition directed at the subconscious.
Directors employed to turn rap videos into infomercials
selling whips, selling chains,
whipping and chaining the children,
incarcerating fathers, damaging the foundation of our villages.

Children search their reflection in the footsteps
of Rappers and Athletes.
Rappers employed to unwrap their innocents
become the circuit breaker of pure truth
and auction their souls off for material pleasure.
Manhood correlates with incarceration;
therefore, private prisons are erected like sand castles
in ghetto playgrounds.
Who profits from this form of LEGAL SLAVERY
and are energized by the powerful energies
currently channeling through our children?
Not in my backyard, I say!

How many LIONS are left standing in these cold lands?

Let your roar resonate throughout the universe.
Take the pens of history from these cold hands,
stare in the eyes of he who oppresses you
and you'll recognize the face as your own.
Freedom is scripted in the skies of your spiritual desert.
CLAIM IT.

Called Back

Drained dry my tear dam,
Still, the cold pain paddles through my heart.
A great leaf ripped from the tree of life
while a new blossom, preparing its part.
We bloomed in seasons of damp sunshine,
doused in puddles produced by dry rain,
absorbed scars that will last a lifetime.
Across my cheeks you bore me a cry stain.
Called to purpose,
like a ripe fruit journeying from its mother's arm,
given only a second to sail with the wind,
before colliding with destiny's charm.
This is Life's hidden whisper,
While another candle is lit in the dark.
The spider stares from a web on a branch,
another spirit returns to the bright spark.

Rest In Peace AYYUB

Branch of Love

Grant me the pleasure to love you in my dreams,
and shape shift as your blood vessel,
so that I may sleep to the sound of your heart.

Rising in Love

We dwell on different mountains in the same region
chasing a colorful vibration call Love.
Caution! whispers mind to heart.
Love possesses power that seeps through
to crumble the fortress of stone
build to secure emotions.
I am reminded daily of the organic chemistry of love
by observing the trees' relationship to sun.
This shows me that I should not be falling in Love,
instead I should be rising in love.
I am but a lonely moth, captured by the light within you.
If it brings me to my death to touch once,
I'd weather the journey through a thousand seasons
reincarnate until I touched every part
of your Godly essence.
I'd name each strand of hair on your head of locs
after our children's, children's, children's, children
so we may rest comfortably in the bed of eternity.
If I should awaken naked and alone,
I shall implode into a shooting star
traveling the distant corners of this galaxy
in search of your love.
Embrace me with spiritual and righteous love,
trap me in your divine essence
that I do not become a falling star.
For we have passed the point of falling in love,
we are now rising in love divine.
If the divine archer is to release me your way,
grip tightly to my passing arrow
as we glide through the dark and broken days of Revelation

and soar into our Genesis.
Allow me to plant the seeds of life
inside of your Garden of Eden
so that we may begin the righteous replenishment.
We will grow beautiful flowers and strong trees
in between the hinges of time.
This way time will never close her door on our love.
My love,
I have seen our forever shining in the cornea of your eyes,
but your every blink takes me back into reality
where I stare at you from a lonely distance.
Now I stand and rise to my love.

Green wood in My Orchard

A green wood grows in the orchard of my heart.
The chirping cardinal knew my spring song
shared my lullaby with the sky.
Clouds formed tears of joy
showered the earth with my bliss.
Our lips were glued by love's paste
while tongues slow danced
to the rhythm of Harare rain.
As the seamstress of love sewed us as one,
I meditated to become one with every rain drop,
to speak my selfish demand unto the dry earth,
begging it to stop its spinning
so that this hour with you would last a life time.
Let our dance not be recorded by the minutes of man,
but in the eternal seconds of the Sustainer of love.
May our bare footprints reach that mile
with our ten fingers welded as one.
I'm entranced by your pious spirit.
No need for words when your heart speaks through your eyes.
Don't draw your curtains just yet.
My secret tears are the morning dew on the leaf
that stares through your window.
Please don't close your curtains to me.
Let not the hourglass sand us into forgotten memories.
Kindred spirits riding the chariot of love
through the universe's womb,
count the stars of the heavens,
the tides of the ocean
to know the offspring our love will produce.

Face in the Well

When the face of your unborn daughter
slowly fades in the well,
her bright eyes now blinding your sight,
her features slowly remolding in the garden you once planted,
her cries once loud and pure
have gone mute in your dreams.
Her giggles haunt your daily thoughts.
The family tree that once stood firm in your vision
decays before your eyes.

In the well of Love and War a crack emerged.

We pray war to leak out,
allowing the power of love to seal our broken well,
but we drown in yesterday's memory,
and are rescued by our guilt.

Oh Divine and Gracious spirit of Ancient,
Present and Eternal,
if it is aligned with your righteous destiny,
let this well of love rise for its purpose.
May it nourish our village to come.
If from this well sprinkles confusion and pain,
let it dry like a drought in the shell of man
and let the season of lust pass over our hearts.

Oh Divine and Gracious spirit of Ancient,
Present and Eternal,
guide me to the garden that will sprout her essence,
her little hands pulling my beard,
her naked gums yearning to chew my locs, her smile,
her beautiful face fading in this leaking well.

Divine Mirror

I stared into the mirrors of eternity and saw a younger man.
Foolish of me to think it was me,
when I carry my father's eyes
and my DIVINE father's spirit.
Internally my higher nature wars with my lower nature,
leaving my heart the casualty.
The wounds are seen in my character, my being.

Do I fall or rise to the eyes of this angel
or hold desperately to the fading line separating love and lust?
This exposes me as bare mortal in the DIVINE'S creation.
I've walked many mountains captured
by their spiritual essence
and meditated on hills rich in beauty.
Is she my fertile garden?
Her eyes, my eternal mirror?
I looked inside of her and saw a younger man.
He carried my eyes and our DIVINE FATHER'S spirit.

Spring Forward

Puberty smiles, love is personified,
calligraphy left by footsteps, legs are nature's pens.
Lines of eternity trail across merging palms,
a soft fire kindles through the night.
New fragrance blushes the spring air.
The pollen knows its mission of replenishment
while we wander in lust, becoming casualties of bribes,
heart's carnage on Spring's battle field,
cicada's chanting lovers' soliloquy
to vibrate the southern trees.

Have we forgotten our season's purpose,
or are we helplessly clutched
in the grip of Solomon's lustful curse?

Final Chapter

I still taste the bittersweet web
of forgotten decades formed between our tongues.
Wise words now foreign to my eardrums,
smiles haunt me in the shadow hours of each day.
Warm energy once my cushion
in these frozen streets of Babylon.
Her touch, I still feel in silent memories.
I hate her like I hate the serpents that slither in our land.
I love her like I love the DIVINE within us all.
On the cold ocean of love,
we sail separately towards our waterfalls.
The sun is now our only magnet,
the only source of energy shared in our distant worlds.
Ten numbers, yet a thousand miles away.
Wounds, which cannot be healed,
Trust, which can never be repaired,
I sadly read the last line of this chapter
as the waterfall carries us to new beginnings.

Love Hurts

We ascended the towers of love,
to stand firm like shoulders against the winds.
We walked down love's road yesterday
and scarred one another with bladed tongues.
Why do we choose to re-route
through this valley of love,
paved with hidden thorns?
If the merging of our souls are for righteous sake,
may our love flow
and grow as vines on destiny.
But if we have become the recipe for each other's destruction,
then we must selfishly protect our hearts,
untie the layers of emotion that bond us together
and let it go.
LOVE
What a word!

Crossroads

A man wounded in a battle with love,
sought advice from two angels placed on either shoulder.

One angel yelled,
Continue down this road of love, you imperfect mortal!
Love this woman with all her imperfections.
Her womb will mold your seed.
Plant your heart in her fertile soil.
For I see a great and fruitful tree
from the harvesting of this union.

The other angel replied calmly,
Her beauty is vibrant like the colors on the peacock,
dangerously beautiful as the ocean waves.
Her inner being glows with nurturing energy,
but in this energy vibrates an uncontrollable rage
fueled by deep pain which burns all who cross her path.
Your thoughtless action will be as the wind,
carrying her rage toward your demise.

The man stood still to meditate,
I love her, he shouted from the peak of his heart.
I love her not, he cried while drowning in his reservoir of tears.
"*Run towards the warmth of her love,*" he whispered.
"*Swim far from her destructive waves,*" he mumbled.

A heavy cloud veiled the pale moon,
a harmonious voice chanted in the distant wind,

Have you forgotten how to read the signs on the road
which brought you to this destination?
Down the road of true love, there lay no rocks for war.

Love Garden

Trust not your outer eye,
it is conditioned to respond to surface beauty.
Listen not to the sweet melody sailing from cursed tongues,
it is designed to penetrate regression within your spirit.
Sleep not with parasites,
for you will wake up decomposed.

Maintain a cool distance from lovers who lack self- control,
for they are a danger to themselves
and are bound for self- destruction.
They will confine you to that path.
Appreciate all who tread into your life,
be it positive or negative,
for they will add to your greatness.

Observe your garden in all seasons,
before planting your seed.
They may love you in the winter,
curse you in your fall,
raise you in the Spring,
and be psychotic in the summer.

We sometimes lose great people in our lives
in order to rediscover our greater self.

Syphere Flower

I have plastered cement and bricks,
contributed to the building in many love ciphers,
and have swam through the tears of a thousand Isis.
Mentally, I have planted love seeds into the fertile earth
and been cut by the thorns of roses.
But never have I been so captured by a flower,
beauty matches her mind,
raspy voice can command many nations
and give birth to many sons.
Oh, I'm trapped in a cipher of love,
a bee yearning for the pollen of this flower.
A syphere flower.

Love Lessons

I released the kite of love today.
Though painful is this vacuum that pulls at my heart,
I am finally liberated from the web of chaos,
and I fly freely with scarred wings.

The Archer knows his mark.
Let no mortal misguide the arrow of healing.
The Archer knows the hearts pain,
for The Archer molds the heart to feel it.

Why do we use the arrows of love to inflict pain?
I may not know what mortals over time have defined,
redefined and concluded as LOVE,
but I do know that Love soaked in materialism
is dangerous for the soul.
It bruises spiritual vision and topples sanity;
it molds us blindly to inner beauty,
causing us to neglect GOD within our partners.

No matter what your partner may say...
Love is not WAR;
Love is not CONFUSION;
Love is not POISONOUS WORDS that scar the soul;
Love is not surface beauty;
LOVE is DEEPER.
So deep, So innocent,
It is found in an infant's heart,
unconditioned and pure,
freshly released from the essence of the heavenly father.

If they only spoke at birth, they could share the secret of love.
The Archer knows clearly

why we grow to love that which is not right for us.
It all ends painfully when we fall to love
or fall in love with someone we do not know.
Rise to the challenge of love-
lust not after looks, surfaced and conditioned.;
Let the soul bleed with beauty;
let the words heal and nurse your growth.
Stare at the essence of that which you love,
and let it go if it is not right for you.
Letting go will be painful,
but you will regain that part of you, neglected
while upon the journey of blind love.

Queen's Games

When playing the game of chess with too many queens,
you may win all of your games
only to defeat yourself.
Pawns can never mimic the footsteps of kings
for a king can step back,
sincerely admit to his errors,
and work diligently to correct his mistakes.
Pray that he does not lose that powerful queen,
with coronet locs wrapping her crown chakra,
who blesses the organic foods in his kitchen,
a queen who meditates with her king to secure him.
The day he loses her,
his sunny kingdom will turn to turmoil:
Castles exposed without protection;
Bishops falling prey to the knights,
While Pawns are picked apart~
Checkmate.

Beauty

If I could dance with only the beautiful parts of life,
she would be my mistress for half a day.
I would spend six hours of that day unveiling her beauty
and tame what beast lay there during the rest.
An old widow warns that pain follows love,
planting itself deep in the fiber of beauty'
I replied,
It is the heart's eye that chooses the companion
and though she may be a sight to behold,
she is not always beautiful.

Silver lining

Your colors still dance on the vibration of my thoughts.
In every motion I tried escaping the painful rhythm
set by your drums,
but my vision forward was besieged by your love,
my heart now beats with yours.
Every beat draws us closer to chaos
and further from our healing post.
As you move on,
take with you the sickle you left in my heart.
Allow me space to burn away the memories
as the dissipating smoke shapes your silhouette.
No matter how hard I push away from you,
I cannot outrun your love cloud hovering above me,
nor cut the thread you have tied to my heart.
You selfishly stained your presence in my thoughts
which haunt me at my bedpost.
So I awaken to face you and welcome your rain,
as I patiently await my silver lining.

Spiritual Beauty

When the caterpillar journeyed inward,
she reemerged with more beauty.

Spiritual Love

Beauty is man's deepest temptation.
Did our path cross for endless hours of seduction
or has the universe granted me a piece of its beloved essence
by way of your presence?
Can the love brought forth through you,
thaw my frozen emotion
and will it promise to numb my heart
tormented with past pains?

As spoken by the wise elders in my village:
Love is the benevolent force that draws together life.
Love is the universal glue,
the world's purest language.
Love reveals its powers through our higher senses
so that we can bring forth new life through our lower ones.
Love owns no reason,
for reasons are the conditioning of lust.

Your love is my soul's magnet,
connecting me to the universal body.
Your love carries an aroma
that birthed life back into my spiritual heart.
I can smell you in my dreams
when the thought of nightmares blur you from my sight.
Suddenly nothing matters more than finding you again.
If this is the universe's way of making a mistake,
then may my next blink be my last.
Like a sea drying into a desert with time,
As does the fragile concept of love man blindly share.

May the watcher of the desert bear us new visions
and may the clouds of love rain forth children

for replenishment.
If our destiny was written by the same hands,
why do you allow your fear to doubt this moment?
Is the blood that flows through our veins
not the ink of the divine writer?
And are our bodies not the pens
that draw poetry for the angels to read?
Know that your journey was inscribed in the sands
of your spirit
and though the footprints leading to your destiny
are sometimes wiped by the wind,
forget not that the inscriber also directs the wind
and every step taken towards love was already written,
so our path merging at this junction is no mistake.
Just hold me and love this moment.

Branch of War

Foolish are they who call on the unholy name given by the serpent, while engaging the serpent in spiritual warfare.

Twins in the Womb

The marine and the missionary,
sailing the ocean marine to capes of unknown.
Is it for bloodshed, is it for baptism?
To the native, the missions are the same.
The warrior wages physical destruction upon command,
while the priest accounts for the mental
and spiritual destruction.
Some natives partake of the tree, while others revolt.
Now the native is renamed.

Roman Reigns

Young minds drilled with subliminal oppression,
innocent eyes raped by pornography.
Humanity growing wild
as country claims liberty and justice for all,
while liberators are tried and hung.
Beaten savagely by the judicial branch.
Regressed into drug addicts, alcoholics, minimum wagers
or simply labeled as "Illegal Immigrant" in lands
taken from their fathers.
Political prisoners rot in federal prisons
with fists clinching and visions of liberation,
while corporate villains invade small villages,
plaguing them with cigarettes,
fast food chains, cheap labor, and alcoholic beverages.
Third world countries thirst to be intoxicated
by wines of western freedom
and sobers to mental and cultural genocide.
Slaves once sipped from the same cups of illusion
and slept nearly 400 years.
Still sleeping in every ghetto while offspring
consider brown and black
the ugliest colors in the crayon box.
Wicked warlords engaged in psychological warfare,
sacrificing innocent sleep walkers in the name of "isms."
17-year olds, child soldiers,
carrying rifles of Mass Destruction,
trained to kill and spill the blood of a faceless enemy,
but too young to consume a cold beer;
too young to drown the ghost of regrets.
A spell has been cast on the meek
destined to inherit the earth
as the "Patriot Act" and "Home land Security"

continues to restrain minds,
incarcerate tongues and silence the voices of freedom.
The sweat of Irish Immigrants;
the cries of Asian American families in concentration camps
after the bombing of Pearl Harbor;
the rainy ashes of Jewish children from Hitler's Holocaust;
The river of Iraqi blood
poured from this western "Freedom" invasion;
the urine leaked down the leg of a lynched slave
and the trail of tears left by the American Natives
have all dried and decayed into a fruit call History
which the children are now feasting on.

9-11-2001

I have tasted the fears of the passing,
evaporating in this hateful atmosphere.
Dark, teary eyes surround me
in search of answers for the images
stained in their impressionable minds.
Though my body sits in this research class,
my soul roams the island of Manhattan.
Hysteria floods the city streets.
The ground trembles beneath me,
silent voices buried alive,
yelling to reclaim what's left of their stolen lives
and search of yesterday's lost smile.
Above the voice of my teacher,
a colorful cloud of sorrowful sounds,
cries creating currents and massive waves:
the Hudson River rising from the tears of mourners.
A great depression is growing in the city's womb,
bombed by hate, marked on the tower's tomb.
War on terror birthed in dark rooms,
the eagle's nest branched with new revulsion,
a new era marked in history.
Freedom as I once knew it will never be the same.
The America I once knew has just opened her third eye-
she now can see her own coffin.

Merchant of Death

Merchants of death,
those Profiteers of destruction who
mimic the tone of peace,
while plaguing the planet with tools for war.
Can the sleeping masses not see the visible stain of this evil?
Can they not smell the stench of hypocrisy
on the serpent's breath?

Burning Bush

In the fogs of a Texas ranch,
A venomous mist seeped deep beneath the earth's crust,
giving birth to a poisonous Bush.
A Bush rooted in wicked colonial intentions,
highly decorated with a regime of warlords.
This Burning Bush produced bitter berries,
split the sea of America.
A MOSES Bush,
one who is divinely inspired for a global capitalist crusade.
He breathed hot winds commanding
leaves on the military branch
to conquer a middle eastern terrain.
First, he redefined invasion as freedom,
pump the capitalist semen through the pipe lines of Iraq,
to impregnate democracy in the womb of the Middle East.
The serpent beast,
stands on the Guadeloupe Mountains in Texas,
region once owned by the Natives,
ordered the late pharaoh Saddam
to *let my consumers go!*
We can find humor in tragedy,
but we don't find the Patriot Act as a moral tragedy,
law officials holding stocks in private prisons,
as an ethical tragedy,
nor do we find American-made weapons of global destruction
as a spiritual and social tragedy.
For that stock on the market can triple your investment,
rescuing your family from financial tragedy;
therefore, you purposely blind yourself
with the ashes of the smoldering Bush,
accepting a Smokey strategy that targets a religion,
tradition and culture that is different from yours,

but it is all justified because it secures the country
from economic tragedy.
In the arena of my mind,
I wrestled with the thought of electing a greater evil
or a lesser evil,
when both were initiated and molded
in the dark dungeons of Yale.
Inside I yell, for I have seen
the offspring of this evil and I agree that this Bush
needs to be severed from its roots.
But the scary truth,
scripted in the sacred scrolls of Revelations
whispers of the ending of a peace,
the birth of a seven headed beast:
Seven nations aligned
to design a plan for global reconstruction,
where humanity will be oppressed under a one world system,
one world government,
one world order;
meanwhile, our sons and daughter's spiritual eyes
are glued to the spell of MTV and BET,
while noses of their parents are captured
by the sweet aroma of the Rose Bush,
whose thorns are wrapped tightly around the neck of another
country.
Maybe when 3,000 more soldiers fall on this bloody chessboard
and that Child left behind
is no longer dazzled by the carrots for this volunteer army.
When the Iraqi women pawn their traditional veils
for spandex and halter tops
and the men trade their robes,
head wraps and traditional wears
for baseball caps and Levi jeans,
and strip clubs are erected in the heart of the Sunni triangle,

causing the rape rate to rise,
liquor stores are planted on every Baghdad block
increasing DUI, homicide, and suicide.
Through CNN we watch the death rate rise,
through the Fox hole we hear the murder rate increase,
and the entire region enslaved under the mark of the beast,
that will transform the Arab man into a credit card number,
the Arab child into a criminal,
paint the Prophet Muhammad (PBUH) white,
teach their children self-hatred subliminal,
maybe then will Bush, and those serpents
hiding behind his shady Bush
look deep in their shallow and shed Souls,
and tell my Amoral America that Democracy works,
our democracy worked,
for Iraq is finally FREE.

Empty Coffins

Old wars and new breath,
my country is at war again.

Old chicken hawks presiding over war chests
in a secret room,
while a young legless vet plays chess in a public park.

The bench carries the smell of his old rifle and duffle bag;
the bench is his new home.

This man bled the essence of life from his wounds
for the ideas and interest of others.
Power corrupts the heart of all
while the patriot falls for the greed of corporations,
still salutes to flags of unknown.

The park is filled with worn and torn eyes.
Razor coated tears
Trickle down the cheek of this homeless veteran.
He lingers in the shadow of Democracy,
while his soul lies in a COFFIN,
draped with a bloody flag.
Still haunted by the bombed infrastructures
where orphans were trapped.
He now sits on the park bench,
drowning in the soulless belly of capitalism.

Benevolence versus Malevolence

A war wages on the shore of every nucleus
of my atomic being.
My ethereal battles with eternity, for my existence;
my spiritual conflicts with Satan, for my soul;
my mental clashes with confusion, for my sanity;
my physical altercations with racism, for my humanity.

Warriors without Wars

Psychologically abused my history,
Conditioned to glorify and romanticize your stories,
Mentally raped my fathers, physically raped my daughters.
Programmed my peers to hate one another,
We slaughter one another
and with angry faces we now stare.
Halted my progressive movements,
taught us to sit on knees and repent,
damaged my unity,
drugged and diseased my communities.
Killed our my moral voices.
Our present day role models are now your choices.
What can I fight for now?
My rage fuels my hunger
and working for you, I don't know how.
I'd love to act off my conditioning
and begin taking from societies' elites,
but then I'd be cage me like an animal
until I'm mentally defeated.
Give me something to fight for,
show me a better tomorrow
and I'll be willing to end my sight for.
My anger can rip holes in titanium doors,
my painful tears have drowned plenty of floors.
Why do we cut each other's faces for respect?
Why are we treating each other with disrespect?
Why are we losing our lives for these crumbs
and why are we proudly bragging about our slums?
What is it that our mothers are crying for?
What is it that we are dying for?
NOTHING!
We are warriors without wars.

Double Bladed Sword

Two sides to the sword.
Technology flirts with spiritual warfare
as HAARP's string cracks earth.
Black holes formed near Haiti
How far will man's curiosity go?

Moon bombed off track in search of water
while Earth's oceans are polluted with mercury.
Red dust covers Australia
attracting tourists from Mars.
Now in Spring, I see Snow.

Glaciers melt at rapid rates,
thawing Ancient species.
Shadows but no bodies,
Mummies, no tombs.
Dimension and vortex,
how deep does the worm hole go?

Galactic treaties broken,
archbishops and archangels,
drone armies and prison planets,
reptiles walk upright.
In the darkest hour the Crystal child glow.

Coat of arms bears the allegiance,
clones and cyborg with artificial feelings,
computer chip and frequencies controlled,
Swine flu on human guinea pigs,
from what heart does this wickedness grow.

Old secrets declassified,
astral-projection spy games,
colorful dreams more vivid,
forgotten glands reactivating,
two suns burn in the horizon.
In which direction will the double bladed sword flow?

Guardians of Time

There is a melody of change in the distant wind
The final trumpet blows, marking the end of a wicked era
Anarchy is the color of these clouds
The coming rain will be a reign of true spiritual freedom

Every spirit is beginning its blossoming
to the arrival of the new sun
Every righteous bone shakes restlessly in the bodies aligned
With nature's ferocious cries
Her teardrops are drum beats to awaken the hibernating giants
Who have slept through centuries of conditioning
While you slumbered
The materialistic greed
Developed a gluttonous appetite

The whispers of revolution echo in the mind of the young
A new breed of warriors is rising
Who no longer desire to be chained by the laws
of Amoral men
The once meek and humble are inflamed with frustration
These indigo youth starved for truth
Now rebelling for change.

The Sword

Warrior of the Greater light,
wield words sharpened by the bladed tongue.
Etymologists of languages
author the unbending truth.
Aware of the dictionaries purpose,
the agent of confusion smiled wickedly and said,

I'm the nomenclature of your words.
I define your diction and pronunciation,
and thus own the objects and style of your speech.
Through the words I designed,
I control the texture of your imagination
with the tone of my tools,
you helplessly define yourself,
your God,
your concepts of beauty,
and your concepts of love.

I smiled righteously and replied,

As the Most High uses his enemies to fulfill his will,
I will gladly use your words to bring down your corrupted system.

Judgment covers the land,
and this is the season of punishment for the wicked.

Your sword is your protection~
Strike down the false ideas that blind you:
your truth is the weapon,
your righteousness is the force.
Thy will be done:

let them with thirst drink;
let them with hunger feast.

Leaves in the Wind

The flowers called me a giant, while the trees just laughed.

FYA BURN

FYA BURN BABYLON!
MAY her institutions of intellectual confusion come down.
MAY she choke from her own lies
and swallow her prescriptions of death.

FYA BURN BABYLON!
May her ashes of evil be seen by all she blinded
and may those ashes rain down
in the sand box of forgotten children.
Her reign of wickedness
consumed their benevolent souls.

FYA BURN BABYLON!
Down to its last brick.
May she be melted by the SUN OF RIGHTEOUSNESS;
be rebuilt by the SONS OF RIGHTEOUSNESS;
re-taught by the DAUGHTERS OF RIGHTEOUSNESS;
and renamed by the TONGUES OF RIGHTEOUSNESS.

Far Away

Oh people,
Yield, while the essence of Allah speaks through the winds.
Let your body be the leaf for the journey.

May you be blown past distant mountains,
far away from the sand of sins,
far away from the land of jinns.

Daydreams

I dwell in a house of illusion
Voices of past
Used to proudly haunt my children's walls
Now replaced with lovers' tunes
Dreams of becoming leaders
Alters into musician's daydream
When poured it into the filter of life
All race down the hole of confusion
Nothing remains solid.

The Beginning

As my rock tumbles through history
in search of its landing,
I am left puzzled by time,
unaware of my standing.

Can the finite truly comprehend
the intellect of THE INFINITE?
Can the INFINITE'S Intellect
function in finite mind?
Can my eardrums translate the tunes that the ants sing?

Like a supreme entity taught to worship mortal deities,
where do I fit in this space and time?
Infinity will never stops her race,
will she allow me time to catch up?
Will she eventually slow her pace?

Life is a cipher
when I cross it,
there, I am told, I will find life's mysterious keys;
there, I am told, I will find the true me.

Symbolism

If man is symbolic to the sun- son (The provider)
Is woman his moon (his reflection) or is she his earth?

Afro Trees

In the morning,
my hair stretches its living arms
for that sun above.
A replica of the trees that surround me,

Those beautiful trees:
Unpicked Afros.
Nature resembles me with her soulful dance.
Afro trees dancing with the wind,
beautiful trees, once proudly they stood.
Now cut from its roots,
perm and fried,
bleached of life.

In the 60's and 70's,
the world wanted to climb my tree.
The world wanted to grow my tree.
What happened to those mighty trees?
When did we lean in the shade of our own trees,
and began admiring the softer grass?

My afro stands with pride,
reddish brown, black and beautiful.
It is alive and continuously growing towards the sun.
The wind blows through the trees,
a leaf lands on my afro to greet its kinfolk.
They laugh,
they share stories.
They are alive.

Grow Up

Even though the games seem set,
the floors are wet,
I must keep walking with my head high.

I've learned that struggles come in pairs
and most babies are born with tears,
but still I walk with my head high.

Life showed me that open minds will open doors.
Closed minds are boxed by time,
confined beneath floors.

We must stop wishing upon falling stars
and start reflecting the lights of our inner sun.
Abide by the Universal laws
expressed gracefully through nature.
It shows us that there is only one way to grow,
and that is up.
SO GROW UP!

Field of Dreams

He harvested in a field of dreams,
one filled with Sheppard, sheep and flocks.
He was dazed by the rainbow's temptation
and dropped his spiritual rock.
He now walks bare foot through the same field,
while being cut by a thorny rose.
A generation of moons eclipsed before his eyes
and the stench of the dead flowers reached his nose.
This left the Sun with no reflection,
with no guidance, with no correction.
Another Old King lost in a bottle,
caught in the wind like a dandelion with no direction.

Sanity

A man once looked outside of himself for a savior:
so the Most High buried him in the core of his soul,
next to the treasures of his wisdom
and untapped insight,
so he could fully absorb his inner wealth.
To the naked eye,
the once sane man suddenly lost his mind.
He walked in circles around the town
for three days talking to himself.
What the people could not see nor feel
was the internal earthquake erupting within the man,
slowly bringing him back to surface,
like a buried diamond.
When the man reappeared with his "Sanity,"
he was more preserved in thought,
polished in physical appearance,
clearer in his speech,
and potent in vision.
A calm, deep glow sat in his eyes,
almost as if the universe stared back through him.

Possess

They worried about what the man possessed,
and overlooked the dark energies possessing the man.
They now follow the man because of his possessions
and they too have become possessed.

Dream Catcher

Is it too late to catch a dream?
My dream catcher un-webbed at spring-cleaning,
dusted by thoughtless daydreams.
How do I hold to my dreams
if I don't remember them?
I have recalled the white season
frost sheltered my nightmares.
Now left on my windowpane is a frozen feather
left by a bird before journeying south.
Can the new sun melt my wintry visions
and fetch a warmer dream?
I only dream it does.

Universal Plea

Souls soaked with sour thoughts
Bitter warrior wombs we seek to find
Daddy's doctrine haunting children's bones
Premature views become hardened stones
Mental incest performed on innocent minds
Impoverished battlefields from which we fought
Drowned cultures lost at sea
Traditions melted in chambers of gas
Snowy ashes tell the tale
History replaced with images of pale
Bombed churches and ghostly mass
The universe shivers as mankind pleas.

Solution Time

A call to action

As we were taught, there are 24 hours in a day, 168 hours in a week, and roughly 720 hours in a month. Every person reading this page can dedicate 1 hour out of his or her your busy month and take on this challenge. You can do it alone, or you can take 2-5 of your closest friends or neighbors. Amongst the group, donate 5-6 dollars total, buy a box of garbage bags, or find some old gloves.

You can begin with your community or the closest community near you in need of cleaning. If you wish to make this a massive project, place a flyer in the mailboxes or at the doors of the residences in your community and inform them of the day and time the project will take place. Again, this will only take one hour out of your busy month to help instill pride back into your community. If this becomes a successful campaign, you can add community gardening and even go as far as organizing community meetings to address real issues in the community.

If we continue to wait for others to fix, or address our issues, this cycle will continue. This challenge is designed to bring the strength and concerns of the community back into the hands of the community. We have to become the change we want to implement. Lead not by your words, but by your example. If you build it, you will attract like minds from within the community to join you. Consistency is the key for community success. After the success of the first month, mark this monthly event into your calendar. Call it COMMUNITY DAY. Let it grow from there. "You can be a part of the problem or the solution"

Four Moves

Four steps to victory,
Two huge step forward to survey the cloudy battle field.
A strong queen to cushions your right arm for support.
Your spirituality in position,
for your blessing and your queen's protection.
Strike with diligence,
topple the kingdom,
conquer your goals.
Check Mate!

Branch of Inspiration

When the world around you grows dark and desolate,
BE the candle.

Soft Landing

Out of the peeling cocoon
sprouting new wings today,
every color is a chanting memory-
but where will this butterfly land,
Is it the web of a hungry spider,
the wind shield of a passing car
or the hair bun of the little girl on the stoop?

Oh Children

Oh children of a great time
Inspire before you Expire
Stain the pages of history with your pens
Let your words warn as screaming trombones
Before the coming flood

Let your writing hands be guided by your spiritual father
And not your undisciplined lust
Let your heart be the nest of your visions
Grow from the mistakes of your mothers
Learn from the mistakes of your fathers
Change the rhythm that trances you closer to your coffin
Mute the vibrations that bring forth your affliction

Remember your greatness
Remember your fall
Remember to stand again

A million trees will form a forest
You must plant the first seed
A million bricks will erect a great wall
You must plaster the path for the first brick
One rock tossed into the ocean of time will create ripples
Let your ripples be felt

May the words you write
The seeds you plant
And the rocks you toss
Create new waves toward home.

Spiritual Ink

Oh lost poets of a greater time
Remove the web from your pens
Let your ink strike pages with conscious pride
The deaf, dumb and blind are in need of your guidance
Sleeping spirits await their awakening through your words
Worry not if they digest your poems
Without receiving the proper nutrients

Your pen is the dibble
The words you write and recite are for the planting of seeds
Plant not the seed of lust and death

Let the creator you worship harvest that seed
With waters that we call experience
Let your pens be shovels
Dig, Dig deep, Dig deeper with your words
And create words to raise the much needed trees.

FAMINE

A FAMINE blooms in the land of abundance,
parched drought fills the wells of mankind,
western education poses as salvation
with delusive doctrines that spew
cycles of spiritual genocide,
and dietary genocide in every kitchen

Oh Lazarus of the West,
detoxify your institutional perceptions.
Burn your degrees of certified death,
for you must be born again.
Put down your unrighteous books of hate,
nail your pervert preachers to their crosses,
for you must truly be born again.

Set your antenna inward,
tune in to the forgotten channel of everlasting life,
digest with holy intent,
drink righteously, love eternally.
Teach truth,
clear the path of your internal walkway
so you may realign with the essence of greatness
breathed into you.

Our thoughts,
our ideas and "profound" concepts
are all shaped by the definitions of ROME/Babylon.
LET HER GO
For she feeds you your FAMINE.
She serves you your droughts
through her institutions of higher education,
her institutions of DEATH.

The Greater You

The river loses its identity
when it discovers the vast ocean:
its depth stretches to unknown measures,
its boundaries untested by the expanse of the island,
its waves uncontrolled and unconquered by man,
you, too, will become one with the greater consciousness.
When you journey your inner ocean,
you will crack your mortal "I" shell,
lose the appetite for material pleasure,
and shed your conditioned identity
for a union with your greater consciousness.

PURE

Nations stand like sand statues
in the midst of the Spiritual storm.
A new hour bows for the children of benevolence.
Study the heavens above and within you.
And be charged with visions of prosperity.

The knees of Goliath are weak,
stumbling toward his tomb,
but he dares not to hide beneath the stone.
For no wicked rock shall be left unturned
in the dawn of this era.

Falling cones confessing the wind's fury,
the burning hour branded on the limbs of the young,
the trees of tomorrow bare fearless fruits,
ancient roots realigned with the sun.

You were placed in the lake of fire
to sterilize your materialistic souls,
though struck down on the battlefield,
you shall carry on!
March forward with purpose.
We shall carry on!
Till destiny be our resting place.

Message in a Bottle

As I sail through the streams of the shadow of death, I shall fear no
wave, I shall fear no evil.

Divine is the archer who sent me forth with this mission.
I am a concept
an idea trapped in a cold bottle.
Carved on my burning flesh is a message urgent
for humanity is plundering into darker days.
This bottle, I once believed to have captured me,
is now transformed into my ship.
It is my fortress, my vehicle,
as I sail through seas with subtle snakes;
swim in cold rivers full of racist rats;
float through hot lakes with lazy leeches;
and crawl in ponds with corporate piranhas
nibbling at the corpse of my precious seeds.

Divine is the archer that sent me forth with this mission
In this vast ocean,

I will be met with waves of confusion.
I will encounter and properly challenge the minds of our youth
caged with illusions
on sands with footless prints.
Deaf are the flocks that follow the blind Sheppard,
naive are the sheep that follow wolves.
For this cause, I pray I make it to the shores of famine.
I pray for swifter waves.
My journey now dances with the breath of the wind,
an element being seduced by man.
She carries me with pure love.
she guides me in my darkest hour,

147

harmonizes soothing tunes from the book of Psalms
and this boundless ocean where I once saw the spirit of ancient
bottles
float lifeless in the streams of the shadow of death,
now dances to the tunes of this message.
We are allies and were charging through the ripples,
hurricanes and tsunamis to flood the shores of chaos.

Divine is the archer that sent me forth with this mission.

All I seek is one worthy soul,
one hand that is unafraid to touch and mold change,
one heart in tune with the drum of change,
one lung to shout the message of change.
Are there any warriors left in these lost lands
or must my bottle sink to purify the ocean's darkness?

Navigator

Fear not oh Navigator,
conquer the Viking of the your sea.
Society is YOUR ocean.
Set your compass inward and sail with caution
around the cape of affliction.
Face the fierce storms that awaits you along the path,
the mountain-size waves that you MUST conquer.

Set your compass with accurate precision.
The smallest miscalculation
will shift your course.
Many ships sail misguided along the journey.
Some are swallowed by the ocean.

One thing unspoken between the wind and the wave
is that a vessel may lose it path.
Be wary of the currents of confusion.
Never forget that you are the navigator of your ship.
Set your compass inward.
Command your helm
and sail towards your DESTINY.

Matriarch

She's the daughter of an eclipsed moon
self-esteem sucked from the root of her stem.
Sadness coats the verbs of her spoken tune.

Oh winds of Mercy,
please blow her back her pride.
The tube of destruction
carries her from her ancestral tide.
Now she hates the broad nose
used to inhale and breathe,
the almond shape of her eyes
that she uses to see.
Her inner mirror is broken
she sees her complexion as diseased.

She's a flower that blossomed from a crack-
infested ghetto,
but she is also the mother of many moons.

She is the daughter of a cold rain,
and all she knows is cold pain.
She's a new flower on the block
that carries old stains.
Born with thorns on her heart
to protect her from cursed hands,
she remains naive to the pressures of life
and slowly drowns in its material quicksand.
She hates herself, she hates that she fears,
the texture of her pale skin and long hair.
Her inner mirror is broken.
She's left with no complexion at which to stare.

She's a flower that blossomed on a curb of a quiet suburb,
but it is her womb that will carry nations.

She's the reflection of a strong earth,
matriarch of the global village,
but she forgot her own worth.
They are blinding her with cut stones, (Diamonds)
conditioning her with self hate.
She tears petals off her scalp,
bleaches and tans her stems to assimilate.

Sister,
learn to love yourselves, like the trees love the sun.
Cherish your inner treasure,
whether you're from the suburb or the slum.

Grandmother Earth,
please breastfeed the world with your wisdom,
Mother moon, claim your rightful place in your kingdom,
Sister stars, twinkle your lights across the universe,
Indigo daughters, preserve your crystals.

You're a flower and you are here to beautify the world.
Grandmothers, mothers, all blossomed from little girls,
so love the birds and the bees, love the ocean and the shore,
love all on the earth's surface, and all in its inner core.
love all in the human family,
but love yourself more.

The Bacteria on the Flower

Your mysteries used to molest my mind
worse than any maze in which I have dwelled.
It was for your treasures,
and your beauty
that many great empires,
mortals and Gods have swelled.
We named your love after whips:
"That brother is whipped."
For whips were known to scar us
and tear us down.
Your seductive energies has been proven
to naturally stimulate our hormones
and elevate our bliss from frown.
Many races tried taming you,
but their passion were not right for you.
And we appreciate that you stood in our corners
when we were not strong enough to fight for you.
But lately,
it seems you have allowed society to influence you
of how I should be loved,
how I should be accepted.
If I do not posses those worthless elements:
fashion labeled as precious--
out of your wet boxes am I ejected.
You've allowed society to convince you
that your beauty is measured by the texture of straight hair
and a complexion of fair skin,
allowing that conditioning to kill that divine dark essence
that exists within.
I cannot speak for all of humanity,
but I know that my image of beauty
was constructed on Egypt's walls.

Today, the descendants curse their thick hair,
wishing they were skinny and tall,
so they could resemble the bottomless mannequins
we find in modern day malls.
Furthermore,
that imitation beauty does not erect the shaft
you've held for centuries,
while sitting by my side overlooking our thrones,
and the next hundred top models are no match
to your luscious thick lips;
your natural seductive body powers
and dark rainbow skin tones.
When will you realize that you control the rhythm of men
and the hum of bees?.
It was your divine entity that brought mighty Rome
down to its pale knees,

Nefertiti!
Please close your treasure box to the world;
stop allowing any man with worthless wealth
and status to dig in.
You must keep yourself mysterious, curious,
keep our minds in constant spin.
This way, we can learn to appreciate your precious jewels
and sexy moans
when you decide to let your Nile's flow.
If a man cannot wake up with you
and appreciate your beauty
without the clown make-up, you must let the clown go.
For I've seen how we've destroyed this earth,
and I'm willing to crown you with my power,
but you must eliminate those filthy Roman ways.
You must wipe the Bacteria off your Flower.

DIG

The village no longer dances
to the spiritual drumbeats of their ancestors.
Unrighteous tunes sail the waves of young mothers
and dock in their children's imagination.
Broken words carried over the heartbeat of young fathers,
eulogizing their degeneration.
Offspring of time sprout slowly with spirits immortalized,
but flesh regressing in cycles of conditioned self- hate.
Flowers now seek their reflection
in the broken mirrors of men.
She stares with sad eyes,
wishing she was clutched by firm hands.
The Most High provides you the shovel
It is you who must summon the patience
and strength to dig within.
Find yourself.

Heaven

Examine your lot on the divine puzzle
Expand your mental frequencies across the English Channel
and Suez canal,
deliver that delicate message engraved in your soul,
share your divine portion.
Enrich the spiritually famished,
conform not to the unclean,
engulf not in erotic decay.

While in Rome,
do not mimic the immoral ways of the Romans,
stand affirmed on the fragile foundation,
chew not the sour grapes of diluted truth,
drink not from their cups of temptation.
Taste not the water of turbulence,
for the season of sweet destruction shall pass.

You are the dibble and the seed
used to bring forth thy Kingdom.
Walk forward with innate innocence
and be the chlorophyll of the new garden.

Fallen Walls

Let the sound of these fallen walls
Reignite the spirit of the dying lions
Uplift the soul of the wounded wolves
Re-spark the flame of the proud panthers
Who were chained to the pages of propaganda
And assassinated by the poisonous pens
And bullets of racist slanders

Only the strong, the disciplined and the wise
Will devour the wisdom within these crumbs
We, the meek, must plant righteous seeds
And grow beautiful villages out of our dark slums

No more will these bacteria kill our precious flowers
No more Roman reigns/rains
No more numerical prisons
Where the Profits/Prophets of men
Are seized and slain

I am a seed of change
Here to harvest the indigo crops to build a new world
I am a seed of change
Here to drain the stone breast of mother liberty
For spilling spoiled milk onto our crystal children

Moses walked for forty days, forty nights, forty years
Through the blazing deserts of North Africa
And begged the pharaoh of Egypt to
"LET MY PEOPLE GO"
Today
I stand in the mechanical deserts of North America

And I beg the people to
LET YOUR PHARAOH GO
Let go of your mortal masters
That lynches you on trees of injustice
With democratic ropes
Let go of their educational institutions
That buries your GODLY identity
In the halls of intellectual smoke
Let go of these wicked systems
That crucifies our prophets on capitalist crosses

Oh lost descendants of Israel and Ishmael
Rise and unify against the serpent that instigates our wars
We may be a million leaves
A thousand different branches
But we are all one tree

Oh sons and daughters of the Most High
Explode from your shells of confusion
Rise and illuminate your greater lights
In this system's shadow by death
It is your duty as a child of the benevolent
To arm yourself with truth

I, too, know the pressure of the prophet Jonah
Slowly drowning in the belly of a whale
The children of Katrina
Drowning in the bottom belly of the eagle
Political prisoner, drowning in the belly of the beast
Swim towards your spiritual freedom
Close your external eyes and open your inner soul

As the great and mighty elephant
Collapses from the absence of water

So do the people from their spiritual wells drained dry
To know that one sip will rejuvenate your eternal strength
Why do you not drink from the fountains of truth?
Instead you'd rather feast from the tables of temptation
Devouring the death that awaits you there

As the caterpillar makes its metamorphosis
When discovering its inner beauty
So will you
When you discover the greatness that dwells within you
ASCEND.

Replenishment

The new Genesis is ours to rename.
We sorrowed in spiritual confusion for too long.
The giant has risen from the slumber
and left prints to seal the four corners of the earth.
The Sphinx's claws are embedded in the land.
Our children,
The sacred pyramids we vow to protect.
Cursed be he that plays with the bones of the dead.
We sprout here through the women of men
to rescue our children,
mentally buried between the frequencies of death.
The resurrection is at hand,
time to ascend through your highest vibration.
We are here for the replenishment,
we are here for the cleansing.
Our mission was sealed in the Akashic records.
Our pride will not be broken.
Our spirit will not be bought.
Humble yourself.
We are here to guide you back to your purest beginning.

About the Author

Lemuel LaRoche is a highly regarded social worker, poet, and entrepreneur. He is known for his unique approach of fusing poetry and chess as a therapeutic model for helping adolescent, family and community development in the Northeast Georgia area. LaRoche's work inspires, empowers and educates audiences of all ages. His mentorship and counseling helps to cultivate and enrich the opportunity for positive change in lifestyle, personal growth and communication. LaRoche earned a graduate degree from the University of Georgia with a Master's in Social Work. He currently works with youth and families across Northeast Georgia.

65717330R00098

Made in the USA
Columbia, SC
14 July 2019